This book is dedicated to the readers
and writers of my community.

A is for ANACOSTIA, the place we call *home . . .*

. . . from my back porch we can see the Capitol's *dome*.

B is for the BIG CHAIR that rises above the *street*. I imagine sitting up high while dangling my *feet*.

 is for my **COMMUNITY**. Whenever I'm *alone*, their smiles, support and hugs remind me that I'm *home*!

D is for the awesome food that I buy at the *DELI*. It makes me lick my lips and rub my *belly*.

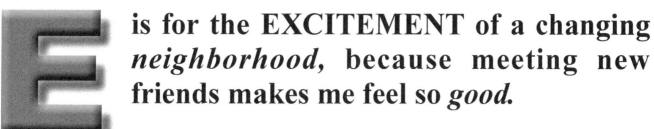

E is for the **EXCITEMENT** of a changing *neighborhood*, because meeting new friends makes me feel so *good.*

F is for **FREDERICK DOUGLASS**, who fought against *slavery*. I'll always respect his courage and *bravery*.

G is for the way that we're all going *GREEN*. Recycling helps keep our neighborhood *clean*.

**is for the HISTORIANS** who keep our memories *alive*. Their love of our history helps Anacostia *thrive*!

is for IHOP, where I eat pancakes and *waffles* with syrup and whipped cream and fruit by the *mouthfuls!*

J is for JUMP ROPE, either one or *two*. As I jump high I try to touch the sky — can *you*?

 **is for the KITES that fly high above my** *head*, **coloring the sky with blue, green, yellow and** *red*.

L is for the LIBRARY, where I read my favorite *books* about brave superheroes or pirates with *hooks*!

M is for the Anacostia Community *MUSEUM*. Whenever there are new exhibits, I can't wait to *see 'em*!

 **is for cool NEIGHBORS like Mrs. Wade and *Mr. Gray*. Helping them is a great way for me and Dad to spend the *day*!**

 is for the "OPEN" sign that hangs on the *door*. When I grow up I want to have my own *store*.

P is for the PARK, my favorite place to *play . . .*

... or stretch out, relax and watch clouds all *day*.

 **is for the QUAINT restaurants and** *shops*. **When it comes to friendly service, these guys are** *tops*!

R is for the RIVER that flows through our *'hood*. *We* try to keep it clean like everyone *should*!

S is for **SUPERMARKET**, where Mom buys us *groceries*, like veggies, frozen foods and fresh-baked *pastries*.

T is for the TENNIS courts where I chase balls with my *racket*. Watch out! Here it comes, and I'm going to *smack it*!

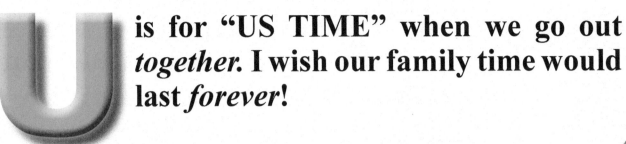

U is for **"US TIME"** when we go out *together.* I wish our family time would last *forever!*

V

is for the VIEW of fishermen having *fun.* **They bait their poles in the afternoon** *sun.*

 **is for the WATER that I splash in the *pool*. On hot summer days it helps keep me *cool*.**

X is for XAVIER, my friend down the *street*. When we sit on the porch Grandma gives us a *treat*.

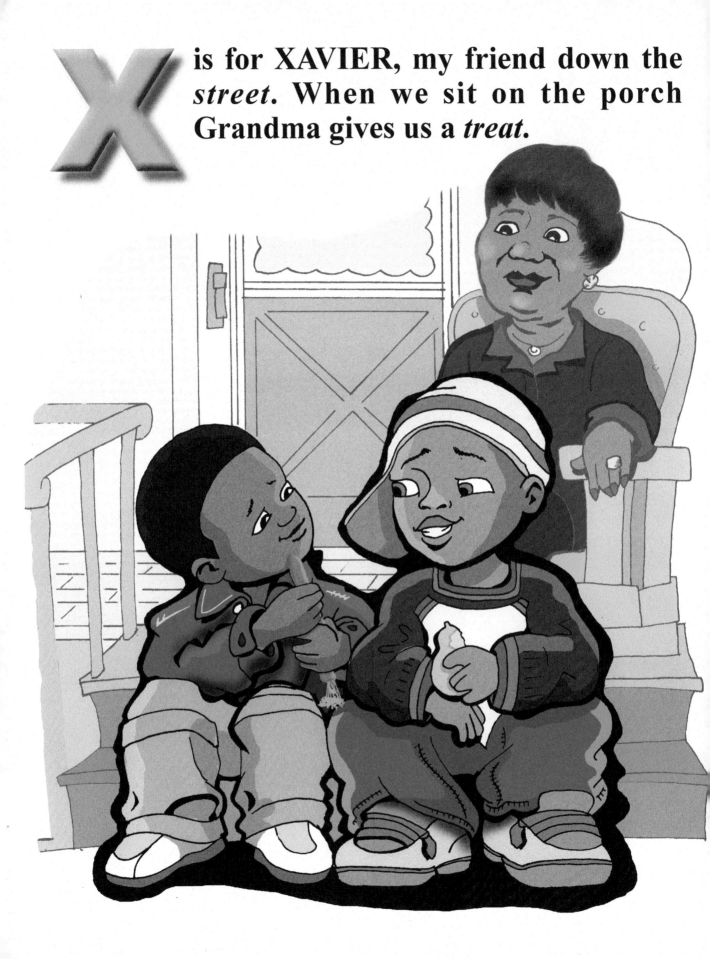

Y is for the YOUTH who show our elders new *things*, like fashion, dance steps and new songs to *sing*.

Z is for my sounds at the end of the *day*. Come back to Anacostia real soon so we can all *play*!!!

A is for ANACOSTIA

ANACOSTIA: A vibrant community located east of the Anacostia River in Washington, D.C. It is a very special place because of the green landscapes, historic landmarks, beautiful views of the city, and the rich stories of the residents. It was an easy decision to move to this neighborhood! Currently, I am a proud resident of the historic community and am surrounded by nurturing, caring neighbors. On summer days, I enjoy sitting on my neighbors' porches chatting about changes in the community and listening to local history shared by elders.

My curiosity is a driving force for many adventures just steps away from my front door. Exploring my community has resulted in many positive experiences and memories that I would love to have both residents and visitors experience. I want them to love their surroundings, to find the culture and wonder on every corner. I want them to see their schools, libraries and community facilities as exciting places to grow, learn and connect. I want them to be engaged in the changes that impact our community.

I want them to love themselves and the people around them. That is why A is for Anacostia and my newest book, S is for South Side, mean so much to me. And I hope they will mean something to you too.

C is for COURTNEY

AUTHOR: Dr. Courtney Davis is changing the perception of inner-city children and telling a different story — one book and one block at a time. Her parents are literacy advocates who nurtured her love of reading by surrounding her with books, magazines and opportunities to create stories as a little girl.

Now all grown up, Dr. Davis is an educator, passionately engaged with urban communities as a practitioner and champion for students, schools and families. This is her first picture book, *A is for Anacostia*, which highlights the lovable children and popular sights of the vibrant Washington, D.C. community.

Her second book, *S is for South Side*, delivers the same heartfelt sentiment to young readers as they journey through the South Side of Chicago, where Dr. Davis grew up and considers home.

Visit Dr. Davis online at www.drcourtneydavis.com

is for JERRY

ARTIST: Jerry Craft has illustrated and/or written close to two dozen children's books and middle grade novels including "The Offenders: Saving the World While Serving Detention!" -- an action / adventure story designed to teach kids about the negative effects of bullying. It was co-written with his two teenage sons, Jaylen & Aren Craft. Jerry's illustrations have also appeared in national publications such as Essence Magazine as well as comic books, greeting cards, book covers, and board games. 2014 marked the release of his first book for Scholastic, called *The Zero Degree Zombie Zone*, written by Patrik Henry Bass of Essence Magazine.

Jerry is also the creator of *Mama's Boyz*, an award-winning comic strip that was distributed by King Features Syndicate from 1995-2013; making him one of the few syndicated African-American cartoonists in the country. Mama's Boyz follows the lives of Pauline Porter, a widow raising her two teenage sons (Tyrell and Yusuf) while also running the family bookstore. Jerry has won five African American Literary Award Show Open Book Awards for "best comic strip" (2013, 2012, 2011, 2009 & 2004).

For more info email him at **jerrycraft@aol.com** or visit **www.jerrycraft.net**

CPSIA information can be obtained
at www.ICGtesting.com
Printed in the USA
LVOW06s1451100117
520451LV00021B/257/P

JAN 2 9 2017